The hen has a nest
in a box in the hut.

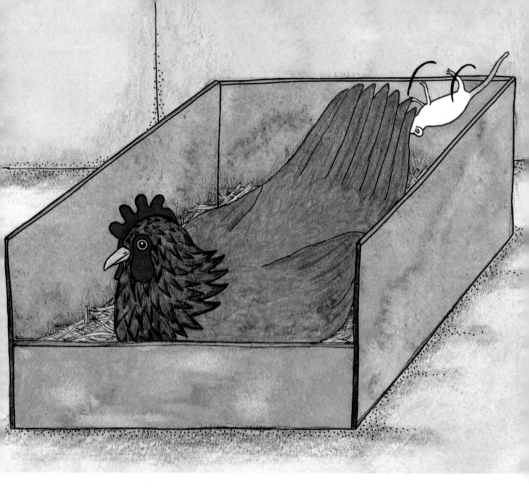

The hen sits on the nest in the box.

The hen gets off the nest.

The hen has an egg
in the nest.

The hen sits on the
egg in the nest.

The hen sits and sits
and sits and sits.

The hen gets off the nest.

Oh no! The hen has a little duck.